Tom and Ricky

and the

Mummy's Crown

Bob Wright

Cover Design: Nancy Peach
Interior Illustrations: Herb Heidinger

International Standard Book Number: 0-87879-327-5

9 8 7 6 5 4
20 19

You'll enjoy all the High Noon Books. Write for
a free full list of titles.

Contents

CHAPTER 1

A Special Exhibit

Tom called Ricky on the telephone. It was early Saturday morning.

"Ricky, the museum is having a special exhibit. They have an exhibit of mummies. Do you want to go?" Tom asked.

"I was going to go to the circus," Ricky answered.

"Wait a minute. The circus is in the park near the museum," Tom said.

"Let's go to both of them," Ricky said.

"How about it? Want to go?" Tom asked. "It would be fun."

"I think I can. I have some things to do at home today. Let me find out," Ricky said.

Ricky left the telephone for a minute. Then he came back.

"Tom, I can go. But I have to do some things here first," Ricky said.

"What if I come by around 10 o'clock. Will you be ready then?" Tom asked.

"I think so. I'll see you then," Ricky said.

Ricky got the newspaper. It told about the exhibit. It said that one of the special things would be a gold crown. The crown had been made for one of the kings.

At 10 o'clock Tom got to Ricky's house. Patches, Ricky's dog, barked when he saw Tom.

"Come on in," Ricky called.

Tom came in. He saw the newspaper.

"Have you been reading about the exhibit at the museum?" Tom asked.

"I sure have. I want to see that gold crown," Ricky said.

"What about the mummies?" Tom asked.

"Well, yes, them, too," he answered.

"Do you have money to get in?" Tom asked.

"What does it cost?" Ricky asked.

"$2," Tom answered.

Patches was wagging his tail.

"No, Patches. You can't go. They won't let you in the museum," Ricky said.

Ricky's mother walked into the room. "When will you two be back?" she asked.

"Sometime this afternoon," Ricky said.

"There will be a lot of people there. Some people will be going to the circus. But people want to see that gold crown," she said.

"We won't be too late," Ricky said.

"Are you going to go to the circus, too?" she asked.

"We will if we have time," Ricky said.

"Watch the time. Don't get home too late. Are you going on your bikes?" she asked. "If you do, be sure to lock them."

"We will. See you later," Ricky called.

"Have a good time," she called to them.

They got on their bikes and left for the museum.

CHAPTER 2

The Museum

It took Tom and Ricky about half an hour to get to the museum. There were lots of people and cars. They found the place for bikes. A lot of people were walking to the museum. They locked their bikes and started walking with the others. They saw a lot of policemen.

"Look at all the people. We'll never get in," Tom said.

"The museum is big. It holds a lot of people. It won't take that long," Ricky said.

"There sure are a lot of police around," Tom said.

"They have to have them. That gold crown has to be kept safe," Ricky said.

Then they saw a long, long line of people.

They got in the long line. It seemed to move fast. There was a woman in front of them. She was wearing a big hat. She also was carrying a small baby. It was all wrapped up.

"That baby is sure quiet," Tom said.

"With all the noise it is still sleeping," Ricky said.

When they got to the place to get tickets, the man said to the woman in front of them, "I am sorry. You can't take the baby with you."

"But I had to bring him. He is so little," she said. The woman's voice sounded funny. Maybe she has a cold, Ricky thought.

"Well, all right. You can go in. The baby won't need a ticket," he said.

Tom and Ricky got their tickets. Then they got in the line to get into the museum. This line didn't move as fast as the ticket line.

A man called out, "We are letting 50 people at a time go into the museum. It will soon be your turn. Have your tickets ready."

The woman with the big hat and baby in front of them was looking all over the place. The baby was still quiet.

"Can we help you?" Ricky asked.

The woman turned around. She looked at

Tom for a minute. She didn't say anything.

Then she turned back around.

*The woman's voice sounded funny. Maybe she
has a cold, Ricky thought.*

"Maybe she's tired," Tom said.

At last the man at the front of the line called out, "We will let the next 50 people in. Have your tickets ready."

"Oh, boy. Now we can get in," Ricky said.

Everyone was moving forward.

The man in back of Tom and Ricky pushed them. They pushed the woman in front of them. She turned around.

"Stop pushing me!" she yelled. Her voice was very low.

At last they were in the museum. There were so many people, everyone was next to the next person. Everyone wanted to see the mummies and the gold crown.

There were many policemen near the crown. It was in a glass box. It was hot in the room. Tom and Ricky tried to get close to the gold crown. The woman with the big hat and the baby was pushing them now. She wanted to get close to the crown, too.

All of a sudden the lights went out. Everyone started yelling. Everyone started pushing. What had happened?

CHAPTER 3

The Missing Crown

There was a lot of noise. People were yelling. People fell down. Tom and Ricky could feel people trying to move. Everyone was pushing someone else. It was dark. Then there was the sound of glass. Everyone was still yelling.

All of a sudden the lights went on. Everyone heard a loud voice saying, "Stay right where you are. No one can leave this museum. The gold crown has been taken."

Everyone was still talking and yelling.

Tom saw Ricky and called him. They saw that the glass box holding the gold crown was broken. Glass was all over the floor. Tom saw a big hammer next to the glass box.

"Everyone, be quiet. We will let you all out, one at a time. Please stay where you are," the policeman called out.

The woman with the big hat yelled, "My baby is sick. I must get out of here."

"Be quiet. We'll let everyone out as fast as we can," the policeman said.

"How could anyone take that gold crown? It must be very heavy," Tom said.

"Well, it has to be somewhere. It isn't in the glass box anymore," Ricky said.

"Look. They opened the door. They are letting people out, one at a time," Tom said.

The woman with the baby was still yelling. "Let me out. I need air. My baby needs air. Let me out."

Then she saw Tom and Ricky. "Can you help me get to the door? I can't get through all these people."

Now the woman seemed nice.

"Women and children can leave first," the policeman called out.

People started to get in a line.

"You can come with me," the woman said to Tom and Ricky. They got in line with her. People started to push to get out.

The police were stopping everyone at the door. The woman kept turning around to look around the room.

"Are you looking for someone?" Tom asked.

"No. I just want to get out of here," she said.

At the door, the policeman said to the woman, "Are these boys with you?"

Tom started to answer, but the woman answered first. "Yes. They are my children. We have to get out of here. We are all sick. Too many people. The room is too hot. Even my baby is sick."

"I'm sorry. I have to stop everyone leaving the museum," the policeman said.

Then someone yelled, "There's a fight!"

Four men in the back of the museum started fighting. People started to push again.

The woman pushed the policeman at the door. He fell back. She pushed Tom and Ricky and ran out. People in back of them ran out.

Tom and Ricky ran with the woman.

"Get away from me!" she yelled. Then she ran over to a long blue car.

"What a day! Let's go home," Ricky said.

Tom was looking at the woman and the long blue car. As she opened the door to get in, her hat came off. And so did her hair. Tom saw it and was very surprised.

"Ricky, that isn't a woman. It is a man dressed like a woman!" Tom said.

The man saw Tom and Ricky looking at him.

Then four other men came running out of the museum to the blue car. The man pointed over to Tom and Ricky. "Get them," he yelled.

CHAPTER 4

The Chase

Tom and Ricky saw the men. They started to run around the cars parked at the museum.

The four men were looking for them. Tom looked up from behind a car. He saw the four men going back to the car.

"Tom, this doesn't make sense," Ricky said.

"Maybe it does make sense," Tom said. "What if the woman—I mean the man—didn't have a real baby? What if this whole thing was planned?"

"Do you think the man with the big hat was holding the gold crown?" Ricky said.

"It could be," Tom said.

"What if the woman—I mean the man—didn't have a real baby? What if this whole thing was planned?"

"Then maybe the men who started the fight were part of the plan," Ricky said.

"I think so," Tom said.

"Quick. Let's get to our bikes. Let's get the number on that car," Tom said.

Tom and Ricky ran to their bikes.

"I think we better tell a policeman," Ricky said.

When they got on their bikes, they saw a policeman. He was stopping people leaving the parking lot.

"What do you boys want?" the policeman asked.

"We think we know something about the gold crown," Ricky said.

"Wait a minute. What are you saying? Did you see someone take it?" he asked.

"We didn't see anyone take it. We think we know who has it," Tom said.

"You better come with me," the policeman said.

"The men we think took it might be leaving right now," Tom said.

"They are in a long blue car. We saw them get in it," Ricky said.

"Did you get the number on their car?" the policeman asked.

"Yes. I did. It was QNS 192. I kept saying it to myself over and over so I wouldn't forget it," Ricky said.

"Good. Now let's see if we can find them," the policeman said.

Tom and Ricky were on their bikes. The policeman ran after them. All of a sudden the long blue car was able to move faster.

"See if you can follow them," the policeman said.

"OK. We'll try," Ricky called out.

"Come back as soon as you can," the policeman said.

CHAPTER 5

The Circus

Tom and Ricky stayed behind the other cars. They didn't want the men in the blue car to see them. If the blue car got onto a big street they would not be able to follow it.

The car didn't get onto a big street. It went a little way through the park. It stopped at the circus.

Tom and Ricky stopped. They hid behind some trees. The men got out of the car. They walked to a small tent with red and white stripes.

The man who had been wearing the big hat was still carrying something. Tom and Ricky could hear the men laughing.

There were circus people walking around near the tent.

They left their bikes under the trees. Then they walked over to the tent.

They could hear the men talking. They didn't know what they were saying.

"I think one of them said something about gold," Tom said.

A clown walked by them and said, "What are you kids doing here? You shouldn't be around these tents. Move along."

"OK. OK. We're going," Ricky said.

"Come on. Let's get back to that policeman," Tom said.

They got on their bikes and rode back to the museum. The same policeman was there.

"What are you kids doing here? You shouldn't be around these tents."

"What did you boys find out?" he asked.

"That blue car went over to the circus," Tom said.

"We followed them to a red and white tent," Ricky said.

"Did you hear or see anything?" the policeman asked.

"I thought I heard one of the men say something about gold," Tom said.

"That isn't much to go on. We should check it out," he said.

"How are you going to do that?" Ricky asked.

"While you were gone we checked on the car. It is stolen," the policeman said.

"Are you going to the circus?" Ricky asked.

"I sure am. Wait. I'll get a car. We'll all go over," he said.

The policeman left. He came back in a police car. "Come on. Get in."

Tom and Ricky got in. They had never been in a police car.

"Are you going to the tent?" Ricky asked.

"No. We'll go to the head man at the circus. That's the best place to start," he said.

The policeman got to the circus office. They all got out and went in.

A big man with a cigar said, "I'm J.B. Wall. Call me J.B. I am the head man of this circus. Can I help you, officer?"

"Yes, sir. We need to find out something about the people in the red and white tent here at the circus," the policeman said.

"The red and white tent? That's the one the clowns use," J.B. said.

"How many clowns work for you?" the policeman asked.

"Five. Why?" J.B. asked.

"Can I talk to them?" the policeman asked.

"Say, is something wrong?" J.B. asked.

"I don't know yet. I need to ask some questions," the policeman said.

"OK. I'll take you over there," J.B. said.

CHAPTER 6

The Clowns

J.B. walked to the red and white tent. The policeman, Tom, and Ricky were with him.

"How long have these clowns worked for you?" the policeman asked.

"They just started two weeks ago. It is a new act. They are very good. People like their act," J.B. answered.

"Why do they have their own tent? Don't all the circus people live together?" the policeman asked.

"They asked for one of their own. They said they liked it better. That was OK with me. And we had a tent they could use. They need to rest because they work hard in front of the people here at the circus," J.B. answered.

They got to the tent. J.B. said, "Come on. We'll all go in. Bert is the head clown."

The five men looked at J.B. and the policeman. They didn't say anything. Then Tom and Ricky walked into the tent. One of the men turned away from them. The five clowns were ready to do their show.

One of them said, "What do you want, J.B.? We have to go and act in front of the people in the big tent."

"This will only take a minute," the policeman said.

"What's going on?" one of the men asked.

"Where have all of you been this afternoon?" the policeman asked.

"Right here. We've been right here all afternoon," Bert answered.

"Did anyone see you in here?" the policeman asked.

"Wait a minute. Why do you want to know that?" another asked.

"Do you know anything about that blue car outside?" the policeman asked.

Then Ricky saw the big hat he had seen at the museum.

"That hat! That's the hat we saw today at the museum, Tom," Ricky said.

"Tell me about the hat," the policeman said.

"That's the hat we saw today at the museum."

All of a sudden Bert pulled out a gun. "All right. Stand still and be quiet," he yelled.

"What's going on here?" J.B. said.

"I said to be quiet," Bert said.

"So. You were at the museum. You do have something to do with the gold crown," the policeman said.

"Tie them up," Bert said.

Just then Tom looked at Ricky. They both ran out of the tent as fast as they could. The man with the gun went to the tent door. He saw Tom and Ricky running. There were too many circus people walking around.

"Let them go. They can't do anything. By the time they get back, we'll be gone," Bert said.

CHAPTER 7

Caught!

Bert had his gun pointed at the policeman and J.B. "Stay right where you are. You aren't getting away like those kids did."

"You'll never get away with this," J.B. said.

"So, you did take the gold crown," the policeman said.

"Tie those two up. And gag them so they can't talk anymore," Bert said.

The other four men got ropes and tied up J.B. and the policeman.

"Come on. Let's get moving," Bert called out.

Bert walked over to a box and picked it up. It was heavy. "Guess what I have in this box," he said to J.B. and the policeman.

Bert and the four clowns walked out of the tent. They went to the blue car and got in it. The other circus people saw them going to the car. Everyone seemed busy.

"OK, Ed. Let's get moving. We've got to get out of here," Bert said.

Ed, one of the clowns, started the car. It wouldn't move.

"What's going on? Why won't the car move?" Bert yelled out.

"Wait a minute. Let me see," Ed said. He got out of the car, looked around, and got back in.

"We have four flat tires," he said.

"Four flat tires!" Bert yelled. "Those kids did it!"

All of a sudden three police cars pulled up next to the blue car. Eight policemen jumped out. They got all around the car.

One of them called out, "Now everyone get out slowly. We won't do anything if you move slowly.

Bert, Ed, and the other three clowns got out of the car. They moved slowly.

"Give me your gun," the policeman said.

Bert gave his gun to the policeman.

Tom and Ricky were in one of the cars.

They jumped out and ran to the tent.

They got out of the car slowly. "Give me your gun," the policeman said.

They saw policemen taking Bert and his men away to jail.

One of the policemen was holding the heavy box.

"We better see just what is inside," he said. He took off the top. There it was. The gold crown. Everyone stopped to look at it.

"I'll take that back to the museum. Tom and Ricky, come with me," the policeman said.

"I'll go, too," J.B. said.

CHAPTER 8

Reward

J.B. got in the police car with Tom and Ricky. It took only a few minutes to get to the museum. The museum was closed. Everyone was gone. The policeman had to get the crown back right away.

"What is this all about?" J.B. asked.

"Well, it seems your five clowns stole that crown today," the policeman said.

"What did Tom and Ricky have to do with all this?" J.B. asked.

"Why don't you tell J.B. all about it?" the policeman said.

"Bert was dressed like a woman. He was holding something that looked like a baby. We thought something was not right because his voice was too low for a woman," Tom said.

"Bert broke the glass case at the museum. He had a big hammer instead of a baby. That's how he broke the glass case. He took the crown and left the hammer there," Ricky said.

"But what did the other four clowns have to do with all of this?" J.B. asked.

"They kept pushing everyone. They were the ones who started yelling. They started the fight," Tom said.

"When the fight started, people pushed even more," Ricky said.

"But they didn't start the fight until Bert was ready to leave," Tom said.

"That's how Bert got out of the museum," the policeman said.

"They were stopping everyone who was leaving the museum. When the fight started, Bert ran out. The other four clowns pushed the other people. They couldn't stop them," Ricky said.

"They thought they were smart," J.B. said.

"They were. But when Bert's hat fell off, Tom and Ricky knew there was something that was not right," the policeman said.

"But they are good clowns," J.B. said.

"They are very good clowns. They have worked for many circuses. But I found out that car was stolen from the other circus they used to work for. That was good that you remembered the number of the car, Ricky," the policeman said.

"What happened to their car?" J.B. asked.

"Why don't you boys tell him?" the policeman said.

"Oh, that. When we ran out of the tent we knew they would have to move fast," Tom said.

"So it was us who let the air out of their tires," Ricky said.

"We ran to the museum for help," Tom said.

"Well, Tom and Ricky. I don't know what the museum will do for you. But here. Take these tickets. From now on when the circus comes to town, you will get in free," J.B. said.

"I'll take the gold crown back in to the museum. You two can go on home now," the policeman said.

Tom and Ricky thanked J.B. Their bikes were still there. When they got home, they had quite a story to tell.